Journeys

Direct Instruction Reading

Level 1

Textbook 3

Siegfried Engelmann

Owen Engelmann

Karen Lou Seitz Davis

SRA

A Division of The McGraw·Hill Companies

Columbus, Ohio

Illustration Credits

Dave Blanchette, Cynthia Brodie, Dan Clifford, Olivia Cole, Mark Corcoran, Susanne DeMarco, Frank Ferri, Kersti Frigell, Simon Galkin, Dara Goldman, Meryl Henderson, Susan Jerde, Anne Kennedy, Pat Schories, and Lane Yerkes.

SRA/McGraw-Hill

*A Division of The **McGraw·Hill** Companies*

Send all inquiries to:
SRA/McGraw-Hill
8787 Orion Place
Columbus, OH 43240-4027

ISBN 0-02-683517-7

2 3 4 5 6 7 8 9 VHJ 03 02 01 00

ch sh th wh

1. wore
2. I'm
3. I've
4. pay
5. turn

1. only
2. tiny
3. funny
4. story
5. really

1. next
2. visit
3. drink
4. pond
5. first
6. six

1. something
2. someone

1

Bitter Butter
Part Three

The little turtle tasted the cake. Did she like the taste? No. She said, "Mom, this cake is not sweet. It is bitter."

Her mom said, "How can the cake be bitter? The batter has fine things in it."

Her mom tasted the cake and said, "Yuk. That cake is bitter."

2

Her mom started to think. After a while she said, "Something bitter got into the cake batter. I think it was the butter. Bitter butter makes the batter bitter."

The little turtle's mom asked, "Who sold you this butter?"

"The brown fox," the little turtle said.

Her mom said, "We will go back and see him. I have something to say to him."

More next time.

sh ch x c s k

1. each
2. beach
3. chase

1. mother
2. another
3. visited
4. pond
5. dove
6. drink

1. nearly
2. dirty
3. really

someone
something

1. swim
2. thinking
3. kids
4. glad

4

Bitter Butter
Part Four

The next day, the mother turtle and the little turtle visited the brown fox. The turtles had a big cake.

The mother turtle told the fox, "We have a cake for you, but you have to <u>sh</u>ow us that you like cake."

The fox lik<u>e</u>d things that w<u>ere</u> free, so he said, "I like it, I like it."

"You told us you like it," the mother turtle said.
"But you have to <u>show</u> us that you like it."

"How can I do that?" the fox asked.

The mother turtle said, "If you eat some cake
really fast, we will know that you like it."

"I can do that," the fox said.

More to come.

7

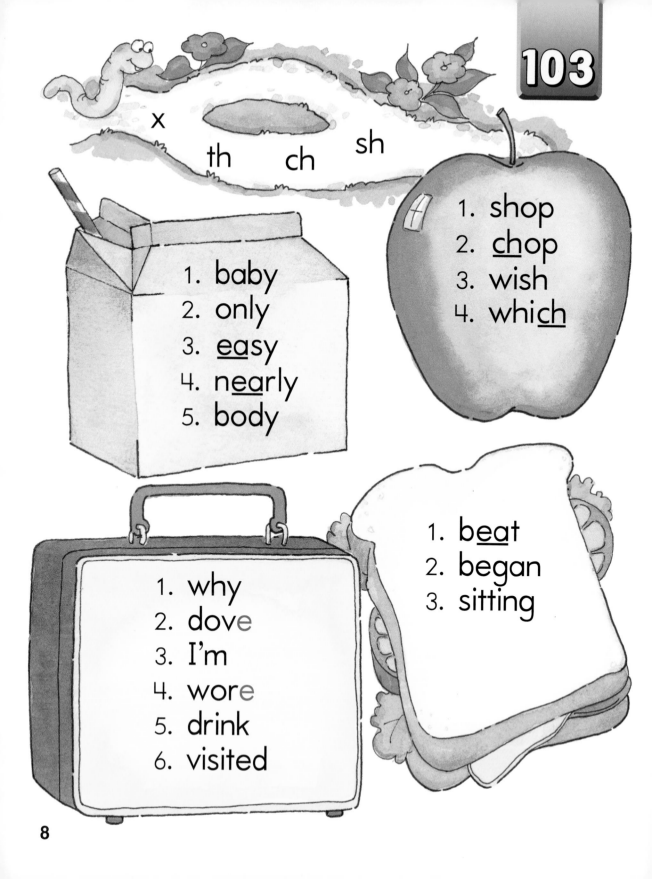

x

th   ch   sh

1. shop
2. <u>ch</u>op
3. wish
4. whi<u>ch</u>

1. baby
2. only
3. <u>ea</u>sy
4. n<u>ea</u>rly
5. body

1. <u>b</u>e<u>a</u>t
2. began
3. sitting

1. why
2. dove
3. I'm
4. wore
5. drink
6. visited

Bitter Butter
Part Five

The mother turtle gave the fox some cake. He ate it so fast that he didn't taste how bitter it was. But after he was done, it started to leave a bad taste.

"Did you like that?" the mother turtle asked.

"I ... I ..." the fox said. "I ... need something to drink."

The fox ran to the pond and dove in. He began to drink and drink, but the bad bitter taste did not go away.

"That cake is bitter," the fox said at last.

The mom said, "Do you know why?"

The fox said, "Oh, it must be the butter I sold you."

The mother turtle said, "Yes, that bitter butter made the batter bitter."

The fox said, "And that bitter batter gave me a bitter taste."

That was the last time the fox sold someone bitter butter.

> The end.

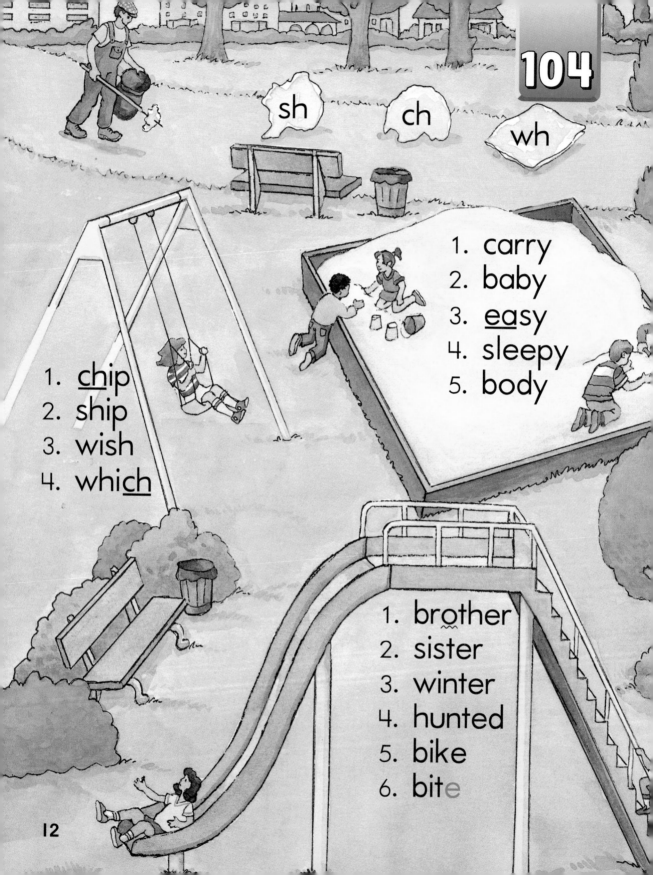

sh   ch   wh

1. carry
2. baby
3. <u>ea</u>sy
4. sleepy
5. body

1. <u>ch</u>ip
2. ship
3. wish
4. whi<u>ch</u>

1. br<u>o</u>ther
2. sister
3. winter
4. hunted
5. bike
6. bite

Pam and the Gold Robber

Pam lived on a ship that had a shop. A robber had a plan to take the gold that she had in her shop. The robber did not know that Pam's gold was not in a big lump.

The robber came to Pam's ship in a little boat. He got into Pam's shop.

As the robber hunted for gold, he said, "I see sacks and rocks and clocks, but I don't see gold."

Just as he was leaving, two cops grabbed him. Later, the cops asked Pam, "Can you show us how you hide the gold?"

Pam told one of the cops to pick up the big lamp. He said, "I can't do it."

The other cop smiled. She said, "I know why. That lamp is made of gold. Ho ho."

The end.

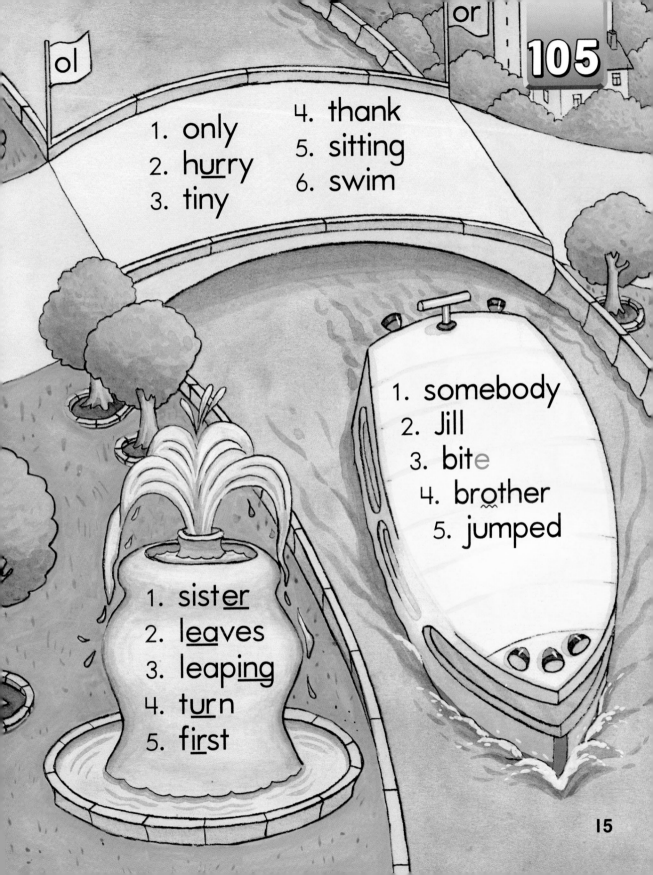

1. only
2. hurry
3. tiny
4. thank
5. sitting
6. swim

1. somebody
2. Jill
3. bite
4. brother
5. jumped

1. sister
2. leaves
3. leaping
4. turn
5. first

The Bug Who Bit
Part One

Jill was a bug who bit other bugs. That's why her brother and sister did not like to be near her.

One day she was playing with her brother and sister. The bugs were leaping over leaves.

It's my turn.

Jill's sister jumped over three leaves. Her brother said, "Now it is my turn."

"No," Jill said. "It is my turn."

Her brother said, "I was here first. So it is my turn."

As he started to take his turn, he said, "Ow. Ow. Ow."

Why did he say that?

Somebody bit him.

Why can't we play?

Jill's brother and sister stopped playing. Her sister said, "We don't like to play with a bug who bites."

Her brother said, "Ow. I hurt."

So her brother and sister ran home.

Jill asked, "Why can't we play some more?"

More to come.

x   b   ar   sh   ch   g

ol   or

1. spring
2. snow
3. pants
4. winter
5. summer

1. I've
2. broke
3. <u>ch</u>omp
4. bigger
5. glad
6. seen

1. r<u>ea</u>ch
2. <u>wh</u>it<u>e</u>
3. sh<u>or</u>t
4. m<u>ar</u>k

We can dive from that tree.

The Bug Who Bit
Part Two

Jill made her brother and sister mad. Her brother said, "Jill bites if things do not go her way."

One day, the bugs were at the pond. Her sister said, "Why don't we go for a swim?"

"Yes, yes," her brother said. "And we can dive from that tree."

"Oh no," Jill's sister said. "We don't know what is in that tree."

Jill said, "If something mean is in that tree, I will bite it."

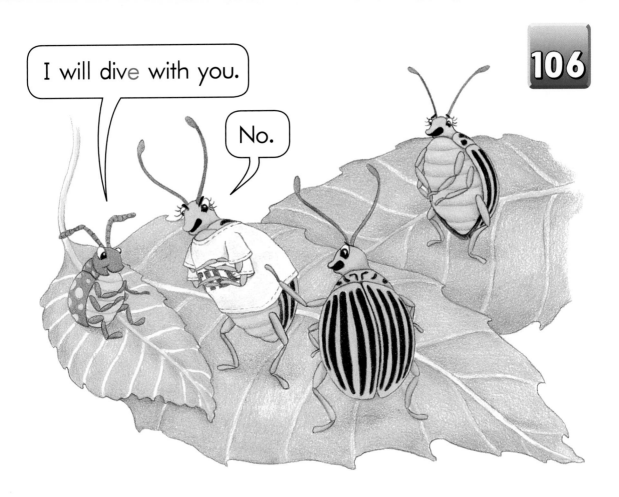

So the three bugs ran up the tree. The bugs came to a little tiny bug who was sitting on a leaf. That bug said, "What are you going to do?"

Jill's sister told him.

The little tiny bug said, "I like to dive. So I will do it with you."

"No," Jill said. "Leave this tree or I will bite you."

This story is not over.

er   ar

b   ch   **107**

1. bite
2. beat
3. bit
4. before
5. broke
6. bigger

1. chomp
2. hard
3. mark
4. white
5. beach

1. hiking
2. diving
3. biting
4. kidding
5. thinking

The Bug Who Bit
Part Three

Jill told the little bug to leave the tree. She
said, "Go away, or I will bite you."

The little bug said, "That is a mean thing to do.
I don't bite other bugs, but I can bite really hard if
I have to."

23

That's how hard I can bite.

Jill said, "Ho ho. You think you can bite hard, but you can't beat me at biting."

Jill ran over to a stick and bit it. Her bite made a little mark on the stick.

24

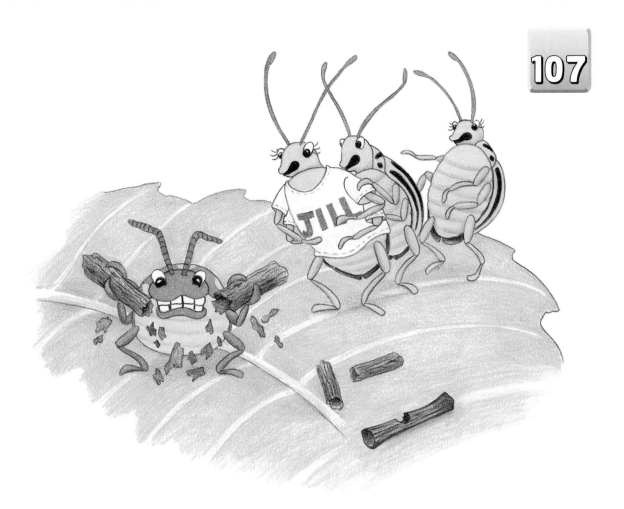

The little bug ran over to another stick and bit it. "<u>CH</u>OMP." His bite broke the stick.

Next, he bit a bigger stick. "<u>CH</u>OMP." That stick broke too.

Jill's sister said, "You can bite like no other bug I've seen."

Jill's brother said, "Yes, and I'm glad you don't bite other bugs."

More next time.

g   d   p   b c

or
ol

1. before
2. somebody
3. sunburn

1. diving
2. biting
3. thinking
4. kidding

1. short
2. told
3. story
4. storm
5. rolling

1. hurry
2. hotter
3. birds
4. pants

My mom told me ...

The Bug Who Bit
Part Four

Jill had just seen a little tiny bug bite two sticks. The little bug said, "My mom told me not to be mean, so I try not to bite bugs. If a bug is really mean to me and makes me really mad, I bite."

Jill was thinking, "I will not make this bug mad at me." So Jill said, "I was just kidding before. I don't bite other bugs. That is a mean thing to do."

Jill's brother said, "Do you mean that, Jill?"

"Yes," Jill said. "Only a mean bug bites other bugs."

Later that day, the four bugs had lots of fun diving into the pond.

After that, one of the bugs said, "Why don't we go hiking?" And the bugs did that.

Those four bugs became pals. And from that day on, Jill did not bite other bugs.

The end.

What Jan Sings

Jan liked to sing, but she made her mother sick of her singing.

One day her mother spoke to Jan. Her mother said, "I like the way you sing, but you sing the same thing over and over. Can you sing other things?"

Jan said, "I like to sing the same thing."

Her mother said, "I will do something for you if you sing more than one thing. What can I do for you?"

Jan said, "Will you sing with me?"

Jan's mom said, "Yes."

Now Jan and her mother sing lots of fine things.

If you are near Jan's home, you can hear that singing.

The end.

Sid Cleans Up the Town

Sid liked things that were clean. But the town he lived in had lots of dirt.

Sid told his mom, "I will make this town clean."

His mom asked, "How will you do that?"

Sid said, "I will make it rain. The rain will clean the dirt away."

"But how will you make it rain?"

Sid said, "I will sing. What I sing will bring rain."

His mom said, "I don't think singing will make rain."

But Sid started to sing. In a little while, the sky got dark and lots of rain came down.

Sid's mom said, "I do not know what to think now."

Sid smiled and said, "I think the town is clean now."

And it was.

The end.

cone   the   fox

e a i

1. winter
2. spring
3. shirts
4. b<u>ea</u>ch

1. your
2. six
3. week
4. bag
5. dock
6. black

1. they
2. ten
3. rent
4. went
5. left

1. <u>ri</u>ding
2. <u>hi</u>ding
3. <u>di</u>ving
4. <u>bi</u>ting

What Jan Makes
Part One

Jan liked to make things, but she made the same thing over and over. On one winter day, Jan's mom showed Jan how to make turtles from rocks.

Jan made the same turtle over and over. At last she had a pile of rock turtles.

Her mom said, "That pile is so big I can't see the rug. What <u>are</u> you going to do with these rock turtles?"

Jan said, "I will pile these turtles on the b<u>ea</u>ch. Kids can play on the pile of turtles."

Make a sh<u>ir</u>t that is not the same.

On one spring day, Jan's mother showed Jan how to make a sh<u>ir</u>t. Jan made five more sh<u>ir</u>ts that were the same as the f<u>ir</u>st sh<u>ir</u>t.

Jan's mom said, "You have lots of sh<u>ir</u>ts that <u>a</u>re the same. Why don't you make a sh<u>ir</u>t for somebody other than you?"

"I will do that," Jan said. "I will make a sh<u>ir</u>t for somebody who is bigger than I am."

More next time.

cake

e

o

1. let
2. ten
3. get
4. they
5. men

1. went
2. rent
3. shirt
4. hurt

1. dock
2. plant
3. black
4. trade
5. cup
6. your

1. before
2. cold
3. shore

Six moms can fit in that shirt.

What Jan Makes
Part Two

Jan's mom showed her how to make a shirt. Jan made the same shirt five more times. After she had made those shirts, she told her mom that she was going to make a shirt for somebody who was bigger than she was.

Three days later, Jan showed that shirt to her mom. Jan's mom said, "This shirt is so big that six moms can fit in it."

Jan said, "I didn't know the shirt was going to be so big. What can we do with this shirt?"

"I think I know," Jan's mom said. "Come with me and I will show you." And she did.

Now, if you go by Jan's home, you may see what Jan and her mom did with that shirt. The shirt is on a car to keep dirt away. It seems to be a fine fit.

This story is over.

fish   bird   under   coat

e i o ar ch ea ai

1. men
2. let's
3. left
4. when
5. went
6. get

1. boating
2. swimming
3. kitten
4. started

1. wishing
2. fishing
3. tell
4. sell

1. lake
2. nine
3. day
4. store
5. each

Ten Men

Ten men liked to do things with each other. When one man went to a show, the other nine men went with him. When one man went to the store, the other nine men went with him.

One day, a man said, "Let's go fishing."

The other nine men said, "Yes, let's go fishing."

So ten men got in a van, and away they went to the lake.

When they got to the lake, the men said, "We will rent a boat." And they did.

Only one boat was left, and it was not a big boat. It was made for three men, not ten men.

The first three men said, "We will get in this boat." And they did.

As they started to leave the dock, the other men said, "We will get in this boat, too." And they did.

Did the boat hold the men? No.

So the ten men did not go boating and did not go fishing. Those men went swimming.

The end.

hat

e a i

z d x b

1. them
2. bed
3. pens
4. red
5. mess
6. when

1. <u>year</u>
2. <u>traded</u>
3. <u>planted</u>
4. <u>sleeping</u>
5. <u>kittens</u>

1. rid
2. sale
3. much
4. Debby
5. week
6. cups

1. five
2. two
3. piles
4. next

Debby Makes Trades
Part One

Debby liked to trade things. She was a fine trader. She said, "When I trade, I end up with more than I had before."

One week, she traded her bike for other things. She got another bike and a sleeping bag and some cash.

She traded the sleeping bag for a cat that had nine kittens.

She traded the kittens for lots and lots of other things. She ended up with her cat, a bird, a ring, three pens, five fish, six cups, two clocks, and the bike she had at first.

She made another trade for some ears of corn.
This corn was not gold like other corn. This corn was
red, and brown, and black, and white. She traded
some of the corn and planted some of the corn.

The next year, she had piles and piles of corn.
Her mom's pals liked that corn. So Debby made a lot
of trades.

More next time.

car toad bug

o e u sh ch ar

1. fine
2. sale
3. may
4. these

1. tell
2. sell
3. three
4. free

1. much
2. rid
3. rugs
4. mess
5. bed
6. them

1. white
2. trade
3. named
4. opened

Debby Makes Trades
Part Two

Debby planted some corn that was not gold. It was red, and brown, and black, and white. The corn came up the next year, and Debby made lots of trades. After she was done trading, her home was a mess.

Debby had piles of things on the rugs and piles of things on her bed. At last her mom said, "You must get rid of these things."

Debby said, "But when I trade, I get more than I had before."

Her mom said, "I will tell you how to get rid of these things. Sell them."

Debby said, "That is a fine plan."

So Debby had a sale, and it was a big one.

When the sale was over, Debby had three ears
of corn, two pens, one fish, and a big pile of cash.

Debby had so much cash that she opened a
store. It is named Debby's. Debby will sell or trade.
So if you have things you don't need, you may make
a trade with Debby.

The end.

bird   man

1. dream
2. liked
3. named
4. over
5. thing
6. sing

1. kept
2. yes
3. get
4. getting
5. then

1. tired
2. same
3. row
4. time
5. late
6. here

We like
rock turtles.

Bob and Jan
Part One

Jan liked to do the same thing over and over.
One time, she made a shirt that she liked. So she
made the same shirt over and over.
One time she made rock turtles over and over.

Jan had a pal named Bob. She told Bob to come over to her home and sing with her. Bob asked his dad, "Can I go over to Jan's home?"

Bob's dad said, "Yes, but you must come home by nine. Don't be late."

When Bob got to Jan's home, she told him, "First I will sing. Then you will sing."

Jan started to sing, "Row, row, row your boat . . . " But she did not sing it just one time. She did the same thing over and over and over.

More next time.

mole   under   coat

1. getting
2. bet
3. better
4. kept
5. sell
6. when

1. only
2. singing
3. tub
4. duck
5. thing
6. cow

1. taste
2. tired
3. year
4. shine
5. boat
6. while

Bob needs a turn.

♪ . . . life is but a dream. ♪

Bob and Jan
Part Two

Jan kept singing the same thing over and over. It was getting late. And Bob was getting tired. But Jan just kept singing, "Row, row, row your boat . . ." over and over.

At last, Jan's mom said to Jan, "Don't you think it is time for Bob to have a turn singing?"

"Yes," Jan said. So Bob had a t<u>ur</u>n. "You are my sunshin<u>e</u> . . . "

When he was d<u>o</u>ne, Jan said, "I like the way you sing. Do it one more time." So Bob did it one more time.

When Bob was d<u>o</u>ne, Jan said the same thing she said before. And Bob did the same thing he did before.

At last, Jan's mom said, "Don't you think it is time for Bob to go home?"

Do you think Bob got home on time? No. He was late. He ran, but he was not home by nine.

Bob will not be singing with Jan for a while.

The end.

ant   cake

y
u
v
x

1. thank
2. think
3. drink
4. sank

1. tasted
2. hope
3. sale
4. y<u>ea</u>r
5. <u>lo</u><u>a</u>ded

1. last
2. sell
3. turtle
4. little
5. her

1. <u>bitter</u>
2. <u>butter</u>
3. <u>better</u>
4. <u>batter</u>

Better Batter
Part One

Last y<u>ear</u>, a fox sold bitter butter to a little turtle. That turtle's mom made cake batter with that bitter butter. The cake was bad, bad, bad.

So the little turtle and her mom made a cake for the fox and told him to <u>eat</u> it. He did. That cake was so bitter that he had to dive into the pond and drink, drink, drink.

I hope it is not bitter.

Then the fox told the little turtle and her mom, "That is the last time I will sell bitter butter."

This <u>year</u>, the fox made a big tub of butter. He said, "I made a lot of butter. I hope it is not bitter butter."

He tasted a little bit of his butter. Then he jumped up and down and said, "This is better than other butter. It is so sweet and fine."

More next time.

clock   will   sing

ar   ir   ch   sh

1. thank
2. thing
3. sing
4. sang
5. wing
6. hang

1. some
2. come
3. done
4. one

1. easy
2. yell
3. filled
4. rolls
5. sale

1. they
2. there
3. here
4. were

Better Batter
Part Two

The fox had made a big tub of butter. Was that butter bitter? No. It was sweet. The fox said, "It will be <u>ea</u>sy to sell this better butter."

So he filled pots and pans with his butter. He l<u>oa</u>ded them into his c<u>ar</u>t. Then he started down the r<u>oa</u>d with his pots and pans. "I have sweet butter for sale," he said.

This butter is better.

Not.

Sweet,
sweet
butter

Five birds were near that road. The fox said, "Do you like sweet butter?"

One bird said, "We know the taste of your butter, and it is not sweet. You sold us some last year. It was bitter."

"But this butter is better," the fox said. "Come over here and taste some."

"No thanks," the birds said. "We don't like the taste of your butter."

So the fox hiked down the <u>road</u> with his pots and pans. At last, he came to a rat. He told the rat that he had sweet butter.

The rat said, "I can <u>eat</u> a lot of bad things, but not your butter. It is too bitter for me."

More to come.

119

baby   plane   cry

ir   er   ur

1. yellow
2. they
3. them
4. best

1. were
2. turn
3. summer
4. first

1. wore
2. roll
3. know
4. throw

1. dress
2. red
3. there
4. rid
5. pigs
6. ducks

Better Batter
Part Three

The fox had sweet butter to sell. Did the birds taste it? Did the rat taste it?

At last, the fox came to some goats. "Sweet, sweet butter for sale," he said.

One goat said, "Last year, I made rolls with some of your butter. Those rolls were so bitter that I had to throw them away."

The fox said, "But this butter is better. Come over and taste some."

The goats just turned away.

Go home with your bitter butter.

The fox hiked down the road to the barn. The fox asked the ducks to taste his butter. Then he asked the pigs, rams, and cows the same thing.

But they just told him, "Go home with your bitter butter."

The fox was sad. He did not know what to do. So he sat down and started to think. Then he said, "I know. I will make a cake for the summer Cake Bake."

And that is what he did.

He first made cake batter. He said, "This batter has better butter. Batter with better butter won't be bitter."

He baked a big yellow cake with his batter, and it was fine.

More to come.

mail

wh

th

ar

ir

1. <u>o</u>nly
2. <u>tasters</u>
3. <u>hurry</u>
4. <u>beg</u>an
5. <u>fly</u>ing
6. <u>summer</u>

1. <u>e</u>ach
2. r<u>ea</u>ch
3. birds
4. red
5. rid
6. wig

1. dress
2. white
3. spring
4. brothers
5. sisters
6. best

Better Batter
Part Four

The fox said, "No one will eat this cake if they know that I made it." So the fox wore a red wig, a dress, and a big hat. He said, "Now they will not know me."

I made that cake.

There were 20 cakes in the Cake Bake. Six cake tasters said, "We will eat a little bit of <u>ea</u>ch cake and see which cake is best."

They ate a little bit of the other cakes. But when they came to the big yellow cake, they ate a lot.

One cake taster said, "I can't stop eating this cake. It is so fine."

Then the other cake tasters said, "This is the best cake we have tasted."

Just then, the fox got rid of his hat, his wig, and his dress. He told the cake tasters, "That is my cake. The batter is made with my better butter."

Sweet, sweet butter

Now the fox makes a lot of sweet butter, and he sells it fast. Birds, pigs, rats, cows, and turtles say that it is the best butter they have tasted.

The end.

she   rock

ol   or

1. sing
2. wing
3. sang
4. hang
5. rang

1. summer
2. sister
3. brother
4. winter
5. hotter

1. pants
2. h<u>u</u>rry
3. still
4. st<u>a</u>yed
5. sh<u>or</u>t

1. sky
2. Tom
3. V<u>er</u>n
4. <u>I</u>rma
5. went
6. set

I have a f<u>ea</u>r of flying.

Can Tom Fly?

It was spring. The other birds were set to fly, but Tom was not set to fly.

Tom had a f<u>ea</u>r of flying. He told his mom, "I can run, and I can r<u>ea</u>d. I can sit, and I can sing. But I do not think I can fly."

Did you see my fast t<u>u</u>rn?

<u>Ea</u>ch day, Tom's brothers and sisters went flying, but Tom st<u>ay</u>ed at home.

<u>Ea</u>ch day, the others came home and told what fun they had. Tom did not have fun.

Then just before summer started, Tom's mom told him, "It's time for you to fly. Jump up on my back and hang on."

He did that. And his mom s<u>ai</u>led into the sky.

Then Tom's mother said, "It is more fun if you hold your wings up."

After he did that, was he still on his mom's back? No. He was not on his mom's back. He was flying. And it was fun.

The end.

swim

wh   ol   or   ch

1. t**ur**n
2. b**ur**n
3. thank
4. sank
5. snow
6. slow

1. <u>waiting</u>
2. <u>began</u>
3. <u>sandy</u>
4. <u>winter</u>

1. five
2. ride
3. white
4. bike
5. r<u>ea</u>ch
6. wore

1. <u>burn</u>ed
2. <u>plann</u>ed
3. <u>sun</u>burn
4. sh<u>or</u>t
5. h<u>ar</u>d
6. <u>pants</u>

Vern and His Burn
Part One

The winter was h<u>ar</u>d and cold. <u>Ir</u>ma and her
brother V<u>er</u>n were waiting for spring. <u>Ir</u>ma said, "We
have not seen the sun for weeks. We have only
seen a d<u>ar</u>k sky."

At last spring came, but things were still cold.

It feels like summer.

After five days of rain, the sun began to shine. The day turned hotter and hotter. Vern said to his sister, "It feels like summer."

Irma said, "I think I'm going to ride my bike to the lake and see the birds."

Vern planned to ride with her. Irma wore a big hat. Vern did not have a hat. He did not have a shirt. The only thing he wore was short pants.

More to come.

stick

I don't get sunburned.

Vern and His Burn
Part Two

Irma and Vern were on the way to the lake. The sun was hot. Irma told her brother, "You are as white as snow. I think the sun may be too hot for you."

"No way," Vern said.

Irma said, "But I know the sun will burn you if you don't have your shirt on."

"Not me," Vern said. "I don't get sunburned."

I will see you later.

After <u>I</u>rma and her brother rode to the lake, V<u>er</u>n stopped at a shore that had a sandy beach. He told his sister, "I think I will l<u>ay</u> on this beach so the sun can make me r<u>ea</u>lly hot."

<u>I</u>rma said, "I am going to the other side of the lake and see the birds. I hope you st<u>ay</u> in the shade."

"I will have fun in the sun," V<u>er</u>n said. "I will see you later."

More to come.

bird

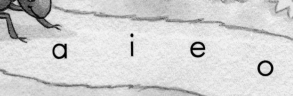

a   i   e   o

1. when
2. then
3. where
4. there

1. red
2. next
3. pink
4. well
5. st<u>ay</u>ed
6. became

1. one
2. once
3. does
4. doesn't
5. wasn't

1. ret<u>ur</u>n
2. <u>a</u>rms
3. h<u>ur</u>t
4. jump<u>er</u>

How do you feel?

I feel fine.

Vern and His Burn
Part Three

As Irma was over on the far side of the lake, the sun got hotter and hotter. Vern did not turn over. He just stayed on the sand. At first, he became a little pink. After a while, he started to get really pink.

At last his sister returned. She asked him, "How do you feel, Vern?"

"I feel fine," he told her. "That sun is not too hot for me."

Later that day, Vern said other things like, "Ow, that h<u>ur</u>ts. Ow, my back h<u>ur</u>ts."

By the time Vern and Irma were home, Vern was not pink. He was red.

Vern's mom said, "You have a bad sunburn. Why didn't you take a shirt and a hat with you?"

Vern said, "I didn't think, but I will think next time."

The end.

mole   dig

1. there
2. they
3. well
4. best
5. yes

1. sail
2. goat
3. play
4. say
5. toad

1. believe
2. Gorman
3. listen
4. wasn't
5. jumper
6. once

1. pal
2. pail
3. liked
4. hiked

The Goat and the Pail

A goat named Gorman did not see well. He liked to play with his pals, but his pals did not like to play with him. They said, "It is no fun to play with a goat that runs into you time after time."

One day, the pals were playing with a pail. One pal was a toad who liked to hop over the pail. The fox liked to jump over the pail, too. The pig didn't jump over the pail. She ate the corn that was in the pail.

Gorman told the other pals, "I can jump over that pail."

The pals said, "We do not think you can."

One pal said, "You say you can jump over it, but you will just run into it."

"No," Gorman said. "I may be the best pail jumper there is." So Gorman jumped.

Did he run into the pail? No.

Did he jump over the pail? No.

What did he do? You will see.

eat   white   leaf   brown

y   g   j   ch

1. any   3. let
2. many   4. wet

1. saw   4. doesn't
2. listen 5. once
3. does

1. legs
2. help
3. wow
4. stand
5. much
6. follow

1. sinking
2. inside
3. harder
4. return
5. getting
6. rolled

Bob and Sid
Part One

One day, Bob and Sid went for a hike. After they hiked for six miles, they came to a cave. Bob said, "Let's go in that cave."

Sid said, "No, there may be mud inside that cave. I hate mud."

My feet are in mud.

My legs are in mud.

Bob said, "Mud can be fun. Let's go inside and see what is there."

So they went inside. It was d<u>ar</u>k. Bob said, "I can't see."

Sid said, "I feel my feet sinking in mud."

"Me t<u>oo</u>," Bob said. "I think my legs are in mud."

118

This mud is getting h<u>ar</u>d.

We must get clean.

Sid said, "It is h<u>ar</u>d to keep going in this mud. Let's go back."

It was r<u>ea</u>lly h<u>ar</u>d, but at last Sid and Bob came from the cave. Bob said, "Wow, that mud on my legs is r<u>ea</u>lly red."

Sid said, "Yes, and we must get clean before that mud gets h<u>ar</u>d."

Bob said, "I think this mud is getting h<u>ar</u>der now."

More next time.

119

his   her   socks   feet

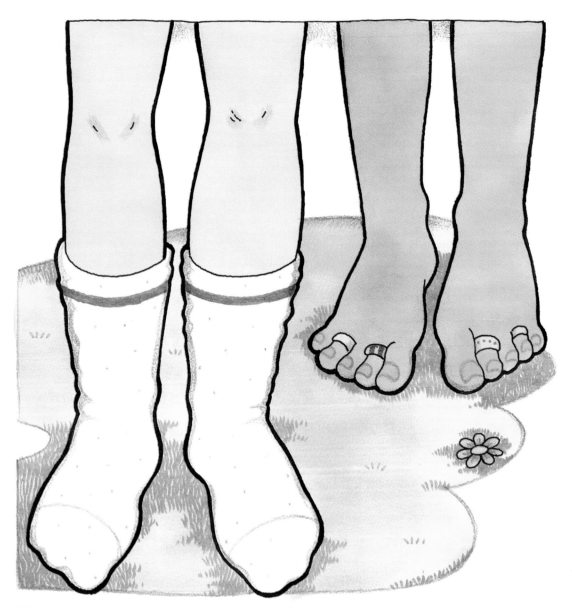

1. shell
2. help
3. wet
4. stand
5. clam
6. close

1. saving
2. silly
3. follow
4. smile

1. does
2. any
3. saw
4. many

1. beach
2. shark
3. shore
4. rolled
5. otter
6. laying

Wow.

Bob and Sid
Part Two

Bob had lots of red mud on his pants. Sid did t<u>oo</u>.
The mud was getting h<u>ar</u>d. The pals had to get rid of
that mud.

Sid said, "I see the beach down the hill."

"How will we get down there?" Bob asked.

"Follow me," Sid said.

How did Sid get down the hill? He rolled. And
Bob rolled after him.

After they rolled down to the shore, they stopped.
Sid said, "My pants are so h<u>a</u>r<u>d</u> that I can't stand up."

Just then, three <u>sea</u>ls came up to Bob and Sid.
One <u>sea</u>l asked, "Why are you laying down like
<u>sea</u>ls?"

Sid said, "We can't stand up."

Bob asked the s<u>ea</u>ls, "Can you help us get into the s<u>ea</u>?"

A s<u>ea</u>l said, "Yes. We can roll you in."

So the s<u>ea</u>ls rolled Bob and Sid into the s<u>ea</u>.

Then a s<u>ea</u>l said, "Now that you are wet, let's swim." And they did.

The end.

leaf   brown

a e i o

1. weed
2. feed
3. shell
4. bell

1. <u>op</u>ened
2. <u>swimm</u>ing
3. <u>happy</u>
4. <u>silly</u>
5. <u>sa</u>ving
6. <u>ott</u>ers

1. clam
2. hunt
3. yelled
4. chase
5. went

1. because
2. close
3. saw
4. shark
5. followed

A Clam Named Ann

Clams seem to have a big smile, but some clams are not happy. One sad clam was named Ann. Why was she sad? She did not like to st<u>ay</u> in the sand with the other clams.

Ann said, "Why can't I swim with the otters?"
Her mom said, "That's silly. Otters eat clams.
They don't swim with clams."

Shark, shark.
Hide, hide.

   One day, a shark was swimming near the clams.
A little otter was swimming near the clams, too. The
little otter did not see the shark. As the otter came
close to Ann, she opened her shell and yelled,
"Shark, shark. Hide, hide."

129

Hang on.

Fun, fun.

The little otter hid in the weeds, and the shark went away.

The next day, the otter came back. She said to the clam, "Thank you for saving me. What can I do in return?"

You know what Ann said, and you know what they did.

So if you see an otter swimming with a clam on its tail, you will know who they are.

The end.

was   rope   rug

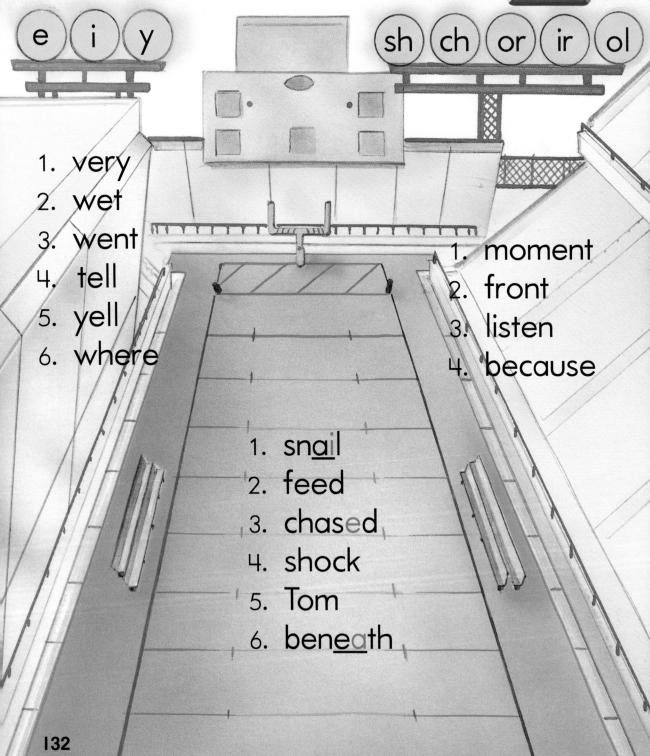

e i y

sh ch or ir ol

1. very
2. wet
3. went
4. tell
5. yell
6. where

1. moment
2. front
3. listen
4. because

1. sn<u>ai</u>l
2. feed
3. chas<u>e</u>d
4. shock
5. Tom
6. ben<u>ea</u>th

Tom and the Shark
Part One

There once was an otter, and his name was Tom.

But Tom didn't listen to his dad or mom.

One day his mom told him, "Don't swim near the caves.

Because there's a shark who hunts in those waves."

But Tom started playing, and he wasn't <u>re</u>ally thinking.

He first chas<u>e</u>d a clam that seemed to be sinking.

Then he follow<u>e</u>d two <u>seal</u>s that were clos<u>e</u> to the shore.

He follow<u>e</u>d thos<u>e</u> <u>seal</u>s for a mil<u>e</u> or more.

At last he stopped to see where he was.
He said, "I saw something swimming the
way a shark does."
   "Oh, oh," he said, as he hid near a weed.
"I hope this is not where sharks like to feed."

More to come.

135

lake   sky   kite

or ir ol ur

e o

1. <u>mo</u>ment
2. <u>ver</u>y
3. <u>him</u>self
4. <u>some</u>one
5. <u>be</u>neath
6. <u>dar</u>ted

1. such
2. fed
3. there
4. send
5. shock
6. shot

1. I've
2. he's
3. saw
4. front
5. sn<u>ai</u>l
6. swam

Tom and the Shark
Part One

There once was an otter, and his name was Tom.

But Tom didn't listen to his dad or mom.

One day his mom told him, "Don't swim near the caves.

Because there's a shark who hunts in those waves."

But Tom started playing, and he wasn't really thinking.

He first chased a clam that seemed to be sinking.

Then he followed two seals that were close to the shore.

He followed those seals for a mile or more.

At last he stopped to see where he was.

He said, "I saw something swimming the way a shark does."

"Oh, oh," he said, as he hid near a weed.

"I hope this is not where sharks like to feed."

Tom and the Shark
Part Two

But the shark came closer and showed many teeth.
And just at that moment, someone yelled from beneath.
"For a bigger meal, you can come after me."
The otter who spoke was Tom's mom, you see.
She swam and she dove and bit the shark's tail.
She told that shark, "You're as slow as a snail."

I've got you now.

The shark chased Tom's mom as fast as a shot.
    And said, "I've got you now." But Tom's mom said,
"Not."
    Just then Tom got a very bad shock.
    His mom just stopped, in front of a rock.

More to come.

snake

ol
or
ar
ch
sh

1. I'll
2. you're
3. he's
4. shark's
5. men's

1. saved
2. smart
3. street
4. chased

1. which

2. slip

3. such

4. blow

1. <u>tractor</u>
2. <u>trailer</u>
3. <u>him</u>self
4. <u>her</u>self

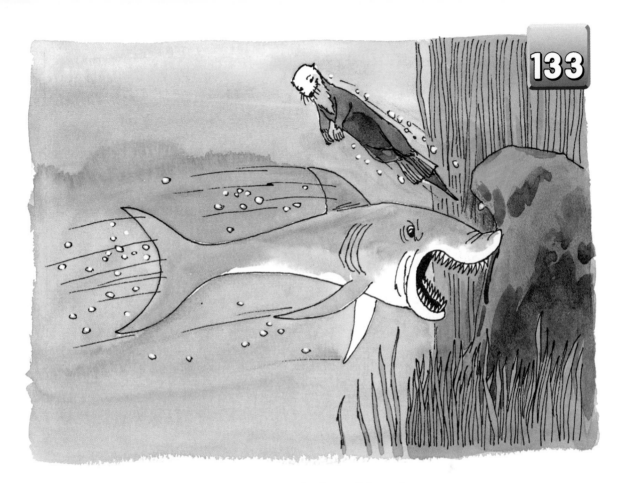

Tom and the Shark
Part Three

The shark chased Tom's mom as fast as a shot.

And said, "I've got you now." But Tom's mom said, "Not."

Just then Tom got a very bad shock.

His mom just stopped, in front of a rock.

As the shark came closer, did she st<u>ay</u> where she was?

No, she d<u>ar</u>ted to one side, the way an otter does.

The shark hit the rock with such a h<u>ar</u>d blo<u>w</u>,
That he said to himself, "<u>Who</u> am I? I don't know."

Then he asked Tom's mom, "Can you tell me <u>who</u> I am?"

She said, "You'<u>r</u>e a very big seal, and your name is Sam."

So Tom has a pal <u>who</u> thinks he's a seal.
And Sam doesn't know that Tom is a meal.

The end.

brown cat

1. Tam
2. send
3. woke
4. rows

1. slipped
2. men
3. left
4. street
5. smart

1. saved
2. hear
3. dove
4. drove
5. driving
6. times

1. every
2. happened
3. telling
4. herself

146

Follow me.

Those stones are neat.

Will Tam Listen?
Part One

Tam's mom told her, "You can hear well, but you do not listen."

Once, Tam and her mom went up a big hill. Her mom said, "Follow me and st<u>ay</u> on the path." Did Tam st<u>ay</u> on the path? No.

She started to play with the stones near the path. Then she slipped and slid down the hill. Ow, that h<u>ur</u>t.

After Tam got home, her mom said, "You have to listen better."

Tam said, "Mom, from now on, I'll listen very well."

But later Tam and her mom went to the lake. Her mom told Tam, "Do not go swimming in the deep part of the lake."

Tam swam in the deep part of the lake. She did not swim very well. So she started to yell for help. Two men dove in and saved her.

After Tam got home, her mother said, "You have to listen better."

Tam said, "Mom, from now on, I'll listen very well."

More to come.

duck   barn

1. <u>some</u>thing
2. <u>any</u>one
3. <u>an</u>other
4. <u>her</u>self

1. c<u>ar</u>t
2. bag
3. left
4. cops
5. sneak
6. drove

1. <u>happens</u>
2. <u>every</u>
3. <u>robb</u>er
4. <u>trailer</u>
5. <u>tract</u>or
6. <u>driving</u>

Will Tam Listen?
Part Two

Tam did not listen to her mom. She kept telling her mom, "I will listen better."

But she still did not listen well. Then something happened that made Tam start to listen better.

Her mom was going to the store. She told Tam, "Do not let anyone in while I am at the store."

After her mom left, a man came by. He said, "I am here to fix your TV."

Tam was going to let him in, but she said to herself, "Every time I do not listen to my mom, something bad happens."

So she told the man, "You will have to come back another time."

The man went down the street. Tam saw him trying to sneak into a home. "That man is a robber," she said to herself. "I must tell the cops." And she did. The cops came and got the robber.

Later the cops told Tam, "You were very smart." And Tam's mom said, "You listen very well."

The end.

will   stick   turn

al or ar ol al ai **137**

1. plant
2. woke
3. steer
4. rows
5. store

1. Jill
2. fix
3. send
4. bags
5. town
6. field

1. driv<u>ing</u>
2. loa<u>ded</u>
3. tract<u>ors</u>
4. trail<u>er</u>
5. wait<u>ed</u>
6. sleep<u>ing</u>

Jill Went to Town

Jill lived on a farm that was six miles from town.
Jill told her dad, "It is time to go to the store."

"Well," her dad said, "I need to fix the car. So I
can't drive you there now."

Jill said, "I have a plan. I can hike to the store.
You can pick me up later."

So Jill hiked to the store. When she got there, she got a <u>cart</u> and filled it. Then she waited for her dad in front of the store. He didn't show up. She began to think of things that may have made her dad late.

At last she saw him. Was he driving the car?
No. He was driving a tractor with a trailer.

Jill loaded her bags into the trailer, and her
dad drove her home.

The end.

short   boat   sail

y e u i o

1. stars
2. hard
3. farmer
4. started

ai al ar al ol or

1. __all__
2. f__all__
3. w__all__
4. sm__all__
5. bang
6. f__ie__ld

1. __sleep__ing
2. __ring__ing
3. __think__ing
4. __fly__ing
5. __dig__ging

1. bells
2. plant
3. steer
4. yard

I will dig rows.

The Farmer and the Steer
Part One

There was a steer who lived on part of a farm.
One day, the farmer drove his tractor to that part of
the farm. The steer was sleeping in the field, and the
farmer did not see the steer.

"I will dig rows," the farmer said. "Then I can
plant corn in this field."

The tractor dug up one row, two rows, and three rows. When the tractor started to dig the next row, the steer woke up.

The steer said, "What is going on? I see a farmer and a tractor in my field. I don't like tractors or farmers here."

The steer got up and said, "I will send that farmer
back to his home."

How will the steer try to stop the farmer?

You will see in the next part of the story.

near   cop

e o al

ol

ar

1. f**a**lse
2. c**a**ll
3. b**a**ll
4. **al**most
5. **al**so
6. **al**ways

1. **someth**ing
2. **fly**ing
3. **land**ed
4. **ring**ing
5. **throw**ing
6. **think**ing

1. f**a**ll
2. bang
3. steer
4. st**a**rs
5. set
6. base

The Farmer and the Steer
Part Two

The farmer was in a field with his tractor. He was digging rows to plant corn in this field. But a steer lived here. And that steer was getting set to stop the farmer. The steer went all the way to one side of the field.

Then the steer ran at the tractor just as fast as a steer can run. The steer was thinking, "I will hit that tractor so hard that it will f<u>a</u>ll over. That farmer will go flying. Then he will leave."

The steer ran into the side of the tractor. There was a big bang. And something went flying. Was it the farmer or the tractor? No. The steer went flying. That steer landed on its back and said, "I hear bells ringing, and I see stars."

The end.

balls   white

ar   al   ch   sh

1. hiss
2. air
3. rags
4. pen
5. never
6. tried

1. call
2. wall
3. ball
4. always

1. baseball
2. throwing
3. missed
4. cars

1. Sandy
2. spark
3. starting
4. streets
5. snow
6. smell

Sandy
Part One

Sandy did not try to do things. She did not know how to throw a ball, but she did not try.

One day, her mom said, "Let's throw a ball and see if we can hit the wall."

Sandy said, "I do not feel like throwing a ball."

One day, her dad said, "Let's go to the lake and throw stones in it. That is fun."

Sandy said, "I don't feel like throwing stones."

Let's throw snow balls.

Another time, her brother said, "Let's play baseball." Sandy said the same thing she always said.

Then one day late in fall, the snow came down. There was snow all over things. The cars had snow on them. The streets had snow on them.

Sandy's brother was throwing snow balls in the front yard. He asked Sandy to play with him.

I hate throwing them.

Sandy went away from her brother. She said to herself, "I hate snow b<u>a</u>lls, and I will not throw them." Just then, a snow b<u>a</u>ll hit her in the back.

More to come.

black   to   spoke

oo ar al ol or

1. yard
2. hard
3. to
4. who

1. everything
2. landed
3. called
4. flames
5. starting

1. sp<u>ar</u>k
2. nev<u>er</u>
3. tri<u>e</u>d
4. missed
5. sent

1. the<u>ir</u>
2. peppers
3. <u>air</u>
4. wall
5. also
6. rags

Sandy
Part Two

Sandy's brother was throwing snow balls in the front yard. He hit Sandy with a snow ball. So Sandy went to the back yard. Then she saw something that was very bad. A spark had landed on some rags. Those rags were starting to burn.

Sandy called to her brother. "Get help," she yelled. "There is a fire next to the wall."

The fire was getting bigger and hotter. The wall was starting to burn.

Sandy said, "I will stop that fire." She made a snow ball and tried to throw it, but she missed the fire.

She made another snow ball and hit the fire.
"Hissss."

She kept throwing snow balls on the fire. At last,
the flames stopped.

Sandy's brother came back with their mom. She asked Sandy, "How did you stop that fire?"

Sandy said, "I will show you."

She ran 20 feet away, made a big snow ball, and sent it sailing in the <u>air</u>. It hit her brother.

He said, "Wow, you can throw."

She said, "Yes. Let's do it some more." And they did.

The end.

licked   ear

ar   oo   al

1. s<u>oo</u>n
2. pool
3. moon
4. too

1. sm<u>a</u>ll
2. pots
3. drank
4. both<u>er</u>
5. b<u>ur</u>p

1. <u>a</u>lmost
2. <u>pepp</u>ers
3. <u>drink</u>ing
4. <u>call</u>ed
5. <u>pile</u>s
6. <u>every</u>thing

1. pen
2. smelled
3. nev<u>er</u>
4. ev<u>er</u>
5. the<u>ir</u>

Peppers for Pam's Pigs
Part One

Pam had six pigs. Their names were Pig One, Pig Two, Pig Three, Pig Four, Pig Five, and Pig Six. Pig Six was very small. The other pigs were three times as big as she was.

One day, Pam was going to feed her pigs. She didn't have pig feed for them. All she had were red hot peppers. Pam had piles of these peppers. She had never fed her pigs peppers, but she said, "I think I can feed my pigs hot peppers. Those pigs eat everything."

So she loaded some peppers in a pot and some peppers in a pan. She went to the pig pen with the pot and pan of peppers. She set the peppers in a pile and called the pigs. "Here Pig One. Here Pig Two . . . ."

And then the pigs came. The pigs smelled the peppers, but didn't start eating. Pam said, "I don't have any pig feed for you. Why don't you try eating these peppers?"

So the pigs smelled the peppers and started to eat.

More next time.

black   white

or

oo

ol

al

ar

1. s<u>oo</u>n
2. food
3. tooth
4. moon

1. bother
2. peppers
3. ever
4. dirt
5. almost
6. burp

1. <u>g</u>etting
2. <u>r</u>olling
3. <u>s</u>a<u>y</u>ing
4. <u>d</u>oing
5. <u>t</u>el<u>l</u>s

1. drink
2. drank
3. t<u>ur</u>n
4. burn

Peppers for Pam's Pigs
Part Two

The pigs were eating Pam's red hot peppers. All at once, Pig Three stopped eating and started to turn red. Then Pig Five turned red. Soon almost all the pigs were red. The red pigs ran to the drinking pan in the pen and began to drink. The pigs drank and drank. Then those pigs ran here and there, eating dirt to get rid of the hot taste.

Burp.

The only pig that didn't turn red was Pig Six. She ate all the peppers from the pot and all the peppers from the pan. When she was done, she was pink, not red. She smiled at Pam and said, "Burp." That was her way of saying thank you.

Now Pam does not feed peppers to all the pigs.
She feeds peppers to Pig Six. And when Pig Six eats
the last pepper, she always tells Pam, "Thank you."

The end.

front   of   back

al
oa
oo
ai
ar

1. waited
2. loaded
3. trailer
4. food
5. soon
6. noon

1. drive
2. drove
3. store
4. miles
5. late
6. home

1. none
2. ok<u>ay</u>
3. because
4. slowly
5. slo<u>w</u>ly
6. tractor

Jill Went to Town for Food

Jill lived on a farm that was six miles from town.

Jill told her dad, "It is time to go to the store for food."

"Well," her dad said, "I need to fix the car. So I can't drive you there now."

Jill said, "I have a plan. I can hike to the store. You can pick me up at noon."

So Jill hiked all the way to the store. When she got there, she got a cart and filled it with food. Then she waited for her dad in front of the store. He didn't show up. She began to think of things that may have made her dad late.

Soon she saw him. He was not driving the car.
He was driving a tractor with a trailer.

Jill loaded all her bags into the trailer, and her dad
drove her home.

The end.

of   front